The Red Rose

by Joy Cowley

In Mr. Singh's garden
was a red rose.

“Ah,” said a caterpillar,
“I see a red rose.”

"Ah," said a bird,
"I see a caterpillar."

"Ah," said a cat,
"I see a bird."

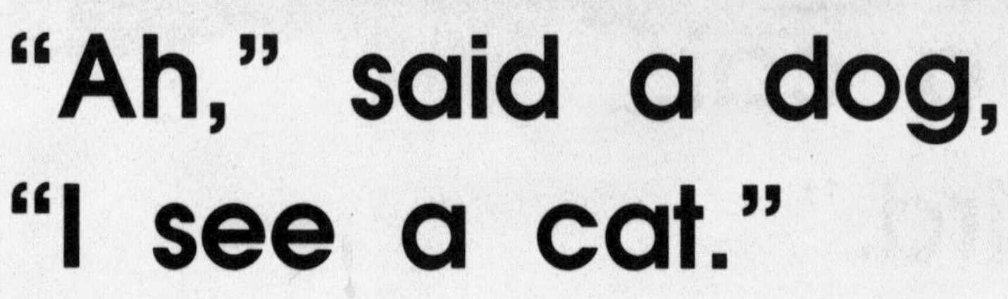

"Ah," said a dog,
"I see a cat."

"Ah," said Mr. Singh,
"I see a dog,
and it's in my garden."

Mr. Singh went outside.

"Ah," said Mr. Singh,
"I see a red rose."

And he picked it.

“Gone,” said the caterpillar, and it went back home.

"Gone," said the bird,
and it went back home.

"Gone," said the cat,
and it went back home.

“Gone,” said the dog,
and it went back home.

Mr. Singh went to Mrs. Singh.
"Happy birthday, my dear,"
he said.

“Ah!” said Mrs. Singh.
“A red rose.”